CLASSIC LANDFORMS OF THE

ASSYNT AND COIGACH AREA

ASSYNT AND COIGACH AREA

TIM LAWSON
Merchiston Castle School, Edinburgh

Series editors
Christopher Green, Michael Naish
and Sally Naish

Published by the Geographical Association
in conjunction with the
British Geomorphological Research Group

Geographical
Association

THE BRITISH GEOMORPHOLOGICAL RESEARCH GROUP

PREFACE

Geomorphologists study landforms and the processes that create and modify them. The results of their work, published as they invariably are in specialist journals, usually remain inaccessible to the general public. We should like to put that right. Scattered across the landscapes of England, Wales, Scotland and Ireland there are many beautiful and striking landforms which delight the eye of the general public and are also visited by educational parties from schools, colleges and universities. Our aim in producing this series of guides is to make modern explanations of these classic landforms available to all, in a style and format that will be easy to use in the field. We hope that an informed understanding of the origins of the features will help the visitor to enjoy the landscape all the more.

Encouraged by the success of the first editions of the Classic Landform Guides we are pleased to introduce this new series, enhanced by colour photographs, new illustrations and with the valuable addition of 1:50,000 map extracts by kind permission of the Education Team, Ordnance Survey. The relevant map for the area covered in this book is Ordnance Survey 1:50,000 Landranger sheet 15. Please refer to the current Ordnance Survey Index for details of the relevant 1:25,000 sheets.

Christopher Green *Royal Holloway, University of London*
Michael Naish and Sally Naish *Hayes, Kent*

CONTENTS

Note on safety

The terrain of this area is rough and often exposed. Footpaths are limited to a few stalkers' paths outside the areas of the Inverpolly and Inchnadamph National Nature Reserves. The weather this far north is often very changeable and can be severe. It is most unwise to undertake any of the excursions covered in this guide unless one is properly equipped with map, compass, waterproof and windproof clothing, proper walking boots, first aid kit and food. In addition, you should tell someone of your intended route and your estimated time of return. Remember, it can take many hours in remote areas such as this for a search and rescue operation to be organised: do not put yourself (and others) at risk.

Cover photograph: Suilven from the slopes of Canisp. *Photo:* Tim Lawson.
Frontispiece: A waterfall in the lower part of the Allt nan Uamh valley.
Photo: Tim Lawson.

Acknowledgements
The author would like to thank the many inhabitants of this beautiful area who have been so kind to him over many years of research; in particular, Peter and Helen Macgregor, whose helpfulness and kindness he can never adequately repay.
Maps reproduced from Ordnance Survey 1:50,000 Landranger mapping.
eproduced by kind permission of Ordnance Survey© Crown Copyright NC/02/12354.
Copy editing: Rose Pipes

Illustrations: Paul Coles

Series design concept: Quarto Design, Huddersfield

Design and typesetting: Arkima Ltd, Leeds

Printed and bound at Stanley Press, Dewsbury

INTRODUCTION

The area covered by this guide possesses some of the most dramatic and varied scenery in North-West Scotland. It straddles the former county boundary between Ross-shire and Sutherland. From Point of Stoer, Eddrachillis Bay and Loch a' Chàirn Bhàin in the north to Ben Mór Coigach in the south, from Enard Bay in the west to the Assynt mountains in the east (Figure 1), everywhere the imprint of glaciation is to be seen. Whether by car or on foot, it is difficult to travel around this area and not become intoxicated by the sheer splendour and variety of landscape at every turn. This guide offers an explanation of a selection of the major landforms and landscapes of this area.

Geology and scenery

The hard-rock geology of this area has been intensively studied, and Assynt is the classic area in which to view the extensive exposures of successive thrust faults and displaced rock slices that are collectively known as the Moine Thrust Belt. Besides the exposure of some of the oldest rocks in the British Isles, this region has some of the clearest evidence for the westward dislocation of rocks that comprises an important part of the structural history of northern Britain. There are a number of excellent publications that explain the local geology to an interested general audience (see 'Bibliography'); it is not the intention to repeat this in detail here, but it is necessary to give a brief overview of the geological history and rock structure as it has such an important bearing on broad aspects of the scenery and the distribution of various landforms.

The oldest rocks are the Lewisian **gneisses**, coarse grained **metamorphic** rocks (more than 2700 million years old) exposed in the rough terrain inland from the coast. They are traversed by **igneous intrusions** in the form of **dykes**, injected into the gneiss between 2400 and 2200 million years ago and trending west-north-west to east-north-east and west to east. These rocks were then subjected to a prolonged period of denudation to produce a land surface of considerable relief. At this time, the region was part of the large land mass that today makes up much of the continent of North America. About 1000 million years ago the climate was semi-arid. Erosion of a mountain range to the west resulted in the deposition of reddish-brown, pebbly sandstones as a series of thick alluvial fans. These were subsequently tilted by earth movements and extensively eroded before being buried beneath more alluvial fan deposits. Collectively, these coarse, pebbly red sandstones are known as the Torridonian (Photo 1). These Pre-Cambrian rocks were gently folded by further earth

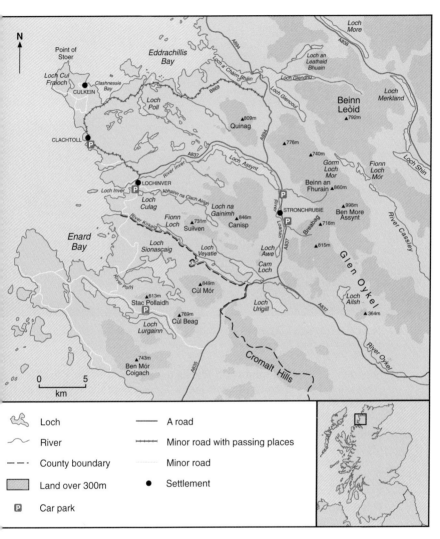

Figure 1: The Assynt and Coigach area: Location of and access to the features mentioned in this guide.

movements, then millions of years later submerged beneath the sea. Marine erosion planed off many metres of Torridonian rock, and on to this near-level surface the earliest Cambrian marine sediments were deposited as the sea got progressively deeper. These sediments now form the False-bedded Quartzite, most often white but locally pink or purple with a glassy, crystalline appearance. They are overlain by the **quartzites** known as Pipe Rock from the tubular structures they contain, the sediment-filled burrows of small creatures that lived on the bottom of this sea. These Cambrian quartzites are succeeded by predominantly fine-grained **calcareous** sediments of which the most

*Photo 1: **Torridonian sandstone hill of Suilven** rising above the Lewisian gneiss surface (viewed from the western end of Fionn Loch). Photo: Tim Lawson.*

important in terms of landscape development now form the Durness group of largely **dolomitic limestones** deposited at the end of the Cambrian period about 450-500 million years ago.

West of the line followed by the Ullapool-Inchnadamph-Kylesku road (A835, A837, A894) this sequence of rocks has been largely untouched by subsequent upheavals in the Earth's crust, except for having been tilted at about 30° down to the east. Geologists refer to this stable area as the Foreland. East of the road there is very clear evidence for remarkable buckling and thrusting of the rocks. A glance at the Assynt geological map sheet shows a complicated repetition of rock outcrops cut by a further suite of igneous intrusions, and the presence of a further group of rocks known as the Moine Schists. These are fine-grained metamorphic rocks that were originally sediments deposited in an ocean to the south and east. They are older than the Cambrian rocks and probably the Torridonian as well, but now overlie them all. These are clear testimony to a period of mountain-building activity about 430 million years ago that saw the creation of the Caledonian Mountains. As an ocean to the south-east closed and the present North American continent collided with what is now Europe, marine sediments and existing rocks were squeezed together and buckled upwards into alpine mountains thousands of metres high. Molten rock welled up into the crust and created the **sills**, dykes and other intrusions that cut through the rocks now making up the Assynt mountains. Four major, horizontally-directed thrust faults (the Sole Thrust, the Glencoul Thrust, the Ben More (or Assynt)

Thrust and the Moine Thrust) were created, along which huge slices of land ('nappes') were displaced westwards. Countless minor planes of dislocation occur between the major thrusts, adding to the thickness of thrust material between the Sole Thrust and the Moine Thrust in the Assynt area (Figure 2).

Since that time, there is no evidence of other periods of rock formation in this part of Scotland. The Atlantic Ocean has opened up, leaving a small part of the former North American continent exposed in North-West Scotland. Differential erosion by running water, wind and ice has removed thousands of metres of rock, wearing down the old fold mountains until only their interiors remain. Lines of weakness in the rocks have been exploited to form valleys and basins, and the more resistant rock types have been shaped into hills. The last 2.6 million years (the Quaternary period) has been characterised by long periods of intense cold (glacial stages) and intervening, shorter warm periods (interglacials). During the numerous glacial stages, ice sheets built up and progressively eroded the land, but each ice sheet removed most of the evidence for earlier ice advances and interglacial periods.

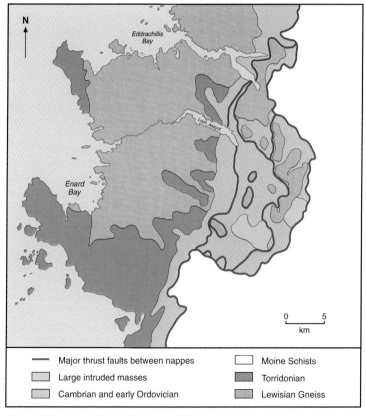

Figure 2: Assynt and Coigach area: *simplified geological map.*

The last glacial stage in Assynt and Coigach

The destructive nature of the glacial stages has ensured that evidence on land for events preceding the development of the last Scottish ice sheet is at best patchy. Layered ocean sediments, composed largely of the remains of minute sea creatures, provide the best record of multiple glaciation in the Quaternary. The relative abundance of particular species tells us whether the global climate was warm or cold. However, the presence of limestone caves in Assynt has created sheltered natural 'rubbish dumps' where additional environmental evidence has been preserved. The solution of the calcium carbonate-rich limestone by acidic rainwater and groundwater results in the redeposition of this mineral within the caves as **speleothems** (stalactites, stalagmites and other flowstone formations). These can be dated from the radioactive decay of minute traces of uranium locked up in their crystal structure when they are formed. As they are only deposited in non-glacial episodes, when groundwater can percolate through the rock, the spread of dates thus obtained can give an indication of when the landscape above was freed from the icy clutches of ice sheets or **permafrost.** Five groups of dates have been obtained from Assynt caves. The oldest group indicates ice-free conditions around 190-180,000 years ago (the penultimate interglacial period of the ocean sediment record), and around 140-120,000 years ago (the last interglacial before the current one). A large number of samples have been dated to the period 95-56,000 years ago, suggesting that there was no prolonged build-up of ice in North-West Scotland in the first half of the last glacial period. Another group of speleothem dates indicates ice-free conditions around 38-26 thousand years ago, and radiocarbon dates on reindeer antlers deposited in the Creag nan Uamh 'Bone Caves' (see pages 43-45) show that these animals were living there between 48-42,000 and 32-22,000 years ago. This implies that the last (Late Devensian) ice sheet in Assynt and Coigach started to form some time after 26,000 years ago, yet had not covered the limestone plateau west of Creag Liath (NC 278153) and Breabag until some time after 22,000 years ago.

Initial glacier build-up is likely to have occurred in **corries** such as those in Glen Oykel (Photo 2) and on the north and east sides of high ground, with ice expanding northwards and eastwards, and channelled southwards down Glen Oykel on to the low ground north of the Cromalt Hills. Discrete glaciers would have merged with the ice sheet building from the south until an ice divide was established somewhere to the east of the Assynt mountains. As high ground was progressively over-topped, ice flowed west and north-west across the area, as testified by the distribution of **erratic** boulders and the pattern of **glacial striations.** The basal ice diverged around major hills as it flowed across the region, terminating somewhere out to sea (Figure 3). At its maximum extent a number of the highest mountains protruded above the Late Devensian ice sheet surface as **nunataks.**

Photo 2: Coirean Ban from the head Glen Oykel. *Note the fluted and hummocky moraines in the valley bottom. Photo: Tim Lawson.*

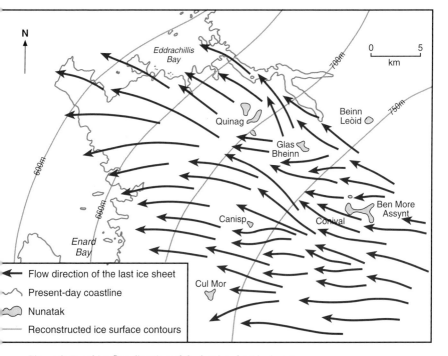

Figure 3: Basal ice flow direction of the last ice sheet in Assynt.

11

South of Coigach the ice sheet achieved an altitude of about 900-930m, declining gently northwards at an average gradient of 8-12m per km. It probably exceeded 810-850m to the east of Ben More Assynt, and has been estimated to be 570-630m thick as it entered Eddrachillis Bay. However, the harshly cold climate that had led to the creation of the ice sheet was also its undoing. As warm ocean currents in the Atlantic were deflected southwards by polar water, the North Atlantic progressively froze over, cutting off the moisture supply to the snow-bearing westerly winds. The last ice sheet was starved of nourishment and started to waste downwards, exposing more and more of the highest land to the extreme cold. Permafrost developed and frost action broke up the exposed rock surfaces, creating **periglacial** landscapes that are still apparent today.

Pollen preserved in basal organic sediment from Cam Loch indicates that a well-established grassland and dwarf shrub vegetation had become established by 13,000 years ago, and hence the ice sheet is likely to have melted away by this time. Around 11,000 years ago a climatic deterioration back to glacial conditions (the Loch Lomond

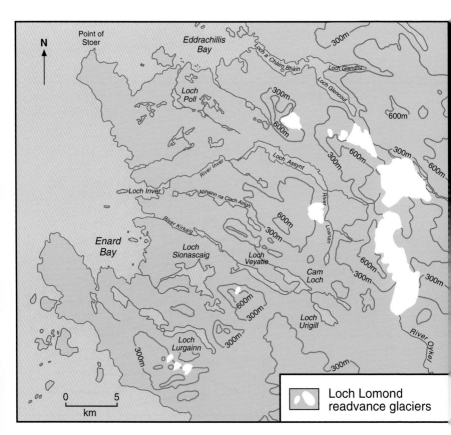

Figure 4: The Loch Lomond Readvance in Assynt and Coigach.

Stadial) resulted in the re-growth of glaciers in the high corries to the north and east of the Assynt mountains and in Glen Oykel, and in a number of discrete locations elsewhere in the area (Figure 4). This Loch Lomond Readvance, as elsewhere in Scotland, was responsible for the creation of many of the most dramatic glacial landforms currently encountered: corries were freshened up, glaciated rock surfaces were re-ground and polished by abrasive particles in the base of the ice, and glacial debris was piled up as **moraines**. Once again, outside the areas covered by glacier ice, permafrost developed down to sea level. Rock surfaces were again shattered by the action of frost, creating rockfalls and the build up of **talus** cones beneath steep or vertical slopes called free faces.

After the ice

However, this glacial episode was only shortlived, as a dramatic increase in mean annual temperatures around 10,000 years ago saw the ice melt, the permafrost thaw and the action of running water take over from ice as the dominant landscape-forming agent. This marks the start of the Holocene, the present interglacial period. Woodland vegetation rapidly developed, dominated firstly by birch and hazel, and then by birch and pine. On steeper slopes, glacial **till** became eroded by streams and transported downhill by **debris flows**, processes that continue to the present day. Rivers have also re-sorted glacial debris, and their channels are floored with gravel and boulders washed out of the **till**. Around 4200 years ago the climate seems to have deteriorated. This cold, moist climate resulted in the start of the build-up of sphagnum moss and peat, and eventually the pine forests were replaced by the expanding heaths. Stumps, roots and branches can still be seen in the basal layers of peat sections. There is no firm evidence that early people played a role in the clearance of this forest, but more recent extensive grazing of the land has helped to maintain the almost treeless appearance of this region. On the highest ground, periglacial processes have continued to play a role in modifying the landscape on a local scale, creating fresh talus below free faces, small-scale patterned ground and **solifluction** features. Around the coast, waves pound headlands and deposit sediment in embayments. The landscape continues to evolve.

Access

The areas described in the following sections can be accessed from the road and partly by footpaths marked on the OS *Landranger* sheet 15, although all the routes will involve some walking over rough and boggy ground. Care should always be exercised when walking on high ground. Weather reports should be checked before setting out, proper walking boots worn and wind- and water-proof clothing carried at all times.

STAC POLLAIDH

Photo 3: Stac Pollaidh from the south. *Photo: Tim Lawson.*

The dominant landscape in the western part of Assynt and Coigach is one of large areas of exposed bedrock with intervening, irregularly shaped lakes, overlooked by isolated hills. This type of landscape is known as 'cnoc-and-lochan' scenery, taken from the Gaelic words for hillocks and small lakes. Its greatest extent is found on the impermeable outcrop of the Lewisian rocks, where knurled hills of gneiss are partly covered by saturated peat supporting grasses, bog myrtle, sphagnum moss and heather. The peat adheres to even the steepest slopes, and stains the waters of the lochans dark brown.

This harsh terrain was created by successive ice sheets whose basal layers were sliding over the bedrock. The ice was therefore able to sweep away broken rock, to pluck at surfaces weakened by weathering in intervening interglacial periods and to use the transported rock debris to scour and abrade the surfaces over which it flowed. The rock outcrops whose structure is inclined towards the direction from which the ice advanced have often taken on the classic *roche moutonnée* shape, smoothed and abraded on the upglacier slopes, but plucked and jagged on surfaces facing the opposite way. It is thought that this landform is most likely to be created where a cavity forms beneath the ice on the leeward side of bedrock protuberances. The stress of being covered by many hundreds of metres of ice causes strain within the rock, resulting in it fracturing in the areas of such cavities. In many parts of Assynt, in areas of 'cnoc-and-lochan' scenery, the graining of the landscape that this causes can give a good estimation of the direction of former ice movement. If one stands looking along the line of ice flow one sees smoothed rock surfaces, but on turning around the view is of steepened and roughened surfaces. Detailed ice flow direction can sometimes be determined where grooving of the rock surface by abrading boulders contained in the ice has occurred, but this is not very common on either gneiss or sandstone surfaces in this region. The action of weathering processes has generally removed any former smoothed, polished surface, and differential removal of weathered minerals has resulted in weaknesses in the structure of the gneiss and bedding within the sandstone being made to stand out. This has created very good friction for the soles of walking boots, but the lineations on the rock surface are **not** glacial grooves and striations.

The northern slopes of Stac Pollaidh provide one of the best of a number of places in the area where one can get a good view across the 'cnoc-and-lochan' landscape. This relatively low (613m) but imposing peak (Photo 3) is composed of Torridonian sandstone, as are its immediate neighbours and those isolated hills to the north, including Suilven whose brooding outline dominates so many of the memorable views of Assynt (Photo 4). From the slopes of Stac Pollaidh it is easy to appreciate that a once continuous cover of Torridonian sandstone has been progressively stripped away from the Lewisian rocks that form the lower ground extending from these isolated hills towards the coast. That much of this erosion was effected by ice sheets is in no doubt when the extent of the bare outcrops of gneiss is laid before you. Much of the gneiss exposure is

Photo 4: A view over the cnoc-and-lochan scenery. Suilven and Loch Sionascaig from Stach Pollaidh. Photo: Tim Lawson.

in fact an exhumed landscape that existed prior to the deposition of the sands and gravels that later turned into the Torridonian rocks, the ice finding the latter less resistant to its action. The carving up of the Torridonian surface into the present discrete hill masses was caused by well defined ice streams flowing in a broadly south-east to north-west direction across this region, cutting a series of **diffluence troughs** (Photo 5), many of which are now occupied by major lakes (e.g. lochs Cam (NC 2113), Veyatie (NC 1813), Sionascaig (NC 1113) and Fionn (NC 1317)). The streamlined shape of Stac Pollaidh (NC 1010), Suilven (NC 1518) and Canisp (NC 2018), emphasises the effect of this areal scouring by discrete ice streams.

From Stac Pollaidh it is also possible to identify another feature of the 'cnoc-and-lochan' topography, namely the effect that major lines of weakness within the gneiss have had on drainage features. Pronounced rock basins and steep-sided valleys, often interconnected by striking gorges occupied by misfit streams, slice right across the area in uncompromisingly straight lines. This structure to the topography is very noticeable on the OS map, and can be clearly seen from the Stac Pollaidh view point. Looking along the length of Loch Sionascaig from right to left one can see a pronounced embayment at its north-west end (Boat Bay (NC 1014)) which continues across the smaller Loch Buine Móire (NC 0915) and along the line of wooded Gleann an t-Srathain. A similar feature contains Loch Veyatie (mostly

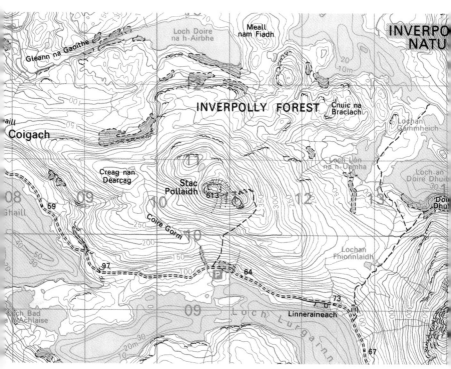

Photo 5: Diffluence trough cut between Cùl Beag and Cùl Mór. Stac Pollaidh can be seen in the background, to the right. Photo: Tim Lawson.

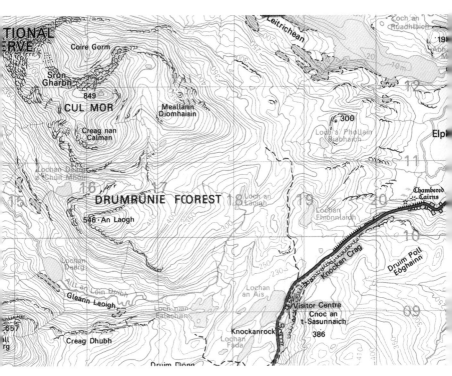

hidden behind Cùl Mór from here) and extends along the line of Fionn Loch to the south-west of Suilven, to reach the coast at Badnaban (NC 075212). These linear features and the countless rock basins that the ice sculpted from the bedrock are not, however, evidence for former ice flow along their long axis. The presence of Lewisian boulders carried up the northern side of Suilven, but absent from the southern side, shows that the last ice sheet to cover the area flowed in a more east to west direction than that suggested by the orientation of this mountain.

Access

Cars can be left in the car park on the northern shore of Loch Lurgainn (at NC 108095), and the eastern end of Stac Pollaidh is gained by following the clear footpath that starts on the opposite side of the road. Much of this path has been recently armoured with boulders to try to prevent erosion to the peat on either side. Please keep to the path. The view described above is obtained from about the 400m contour at approximately NC 113105. There is no need to follow the zigzag path higher than this unless one wishes to climb the hill. The serrated structure imposed by the sandstone buttresses that are clearly viewed from the road makes climbing this hill only suitable for experienced climbers. Descent of the southern slopes from the ridge is extremely steep in places, and covered in loose rocks: it is therefore more prudent to retrace one's steps back along the footpath. Allow about 1½-2 hours for the round trip.

CANISP AND STRONCHRUBIE

The main road (A837) that passes through Assynt follows the valley of the River Loanan before turning north-west to follow the glacial trough containing Loch Assynt. The Loanan Valley follows the outcrop of the Sole Thrust, the lowest thrust plane in the Moine Thrust Belt. To the west of the road lies the Foreland, which has not been subjected to the repeated thrusting that has stacked up great slices of different rocks on the east side of the road, forming the Assynt mountains. The slopes to the west of the road are formed by the gently-sloping quartzite strata rising to the top of Canisp (NC 2018) (Photo 6). Across these slopes successive phases of glacial advance occurred as ice sheets grew and decayed. The quartzite surfaces have preserved very clear evidence of the most recent phases of former ice flow.

Glaciated rock surfaces

Once one has climbed high enough to escape the clutches of the blanket peat, above about 150m, exposed rock surfaces become more extensive. Except where post-glacial weathering has broken them up, these surfaces exhibit very good examples of subglacial erosion features. Two groups of features are present: **glacial friction cracks** and glacial striations. The former are best represented in the

Photo 6: The quartzite dip-slope extending from the Loanan Valley to the summit of Canisp. Photo: Tim Lawson.

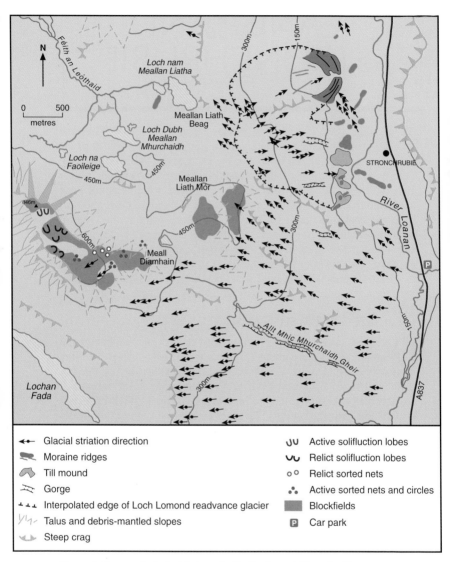

Figure 5: Geomorphological features in the Canisp and Stronchrubie area.

form of hyperbolic cracks, curved cracks whose 'horns' most often point in the direction of ice flow (Photo 7), and crescentic notches, whose 'horns' point up-ice. Their mode of origin is thought to reflect the movement of the large boulders which formed them – hyperbolic cracks forming behind the point of contact of a sliding block, and crescentic notches forming in front of a block that is slightly rotating as it is dragged forward over the rock. Both types of friction crack are most numerous at the crest of small undulations in the rock surface, where shear stresses under the ice would have been at their highest.

Photo 7: Striated quartzite surface. *An hyperbolic crack series is visible just above the camera lens cap. Former ice flow was from lower right to upper left.*
Photo: Tim Lawson.

Glacial striations are abundant, mostly only a few millimetres deep and several to tens of centimetres long. They were cut by rock particles held fast in the basal layers of sliding glacier ice. They are best viewed on damp surfaces with low-angled light, but the presence on the white rock of a dark lichen that has selectively colonised the striations improves their visibility. Their widespread preservation is excellent, and even the deflection of basal ice around small hillocks can easily be discerned. Together with the presence of erratic boulders of Canisp porphyry (Photo 8) brought up the slope from the east, the striations show a dominant regional former ice flow towards the west and north-west, with ice deflected either side of the summit of Canisp (Figure 5). This reflects the ice flow of the last (Late Devensian) ice sheet. In the area to the north-east of Meallan Liath Mór (NC 2319) particularly good striated surfaces can be seen, although these striations indicate local ice flow to the east and north-east, cutting across a weaker set of striations that conform to the regional trend. These indicate a later ice flow down the slope from Meallan Liath Mór during the Loch Lomond Stadial, towards Stronchrubie (NC 247193) in the valley below (Photo 9).

A number of well-defined gorges extend down the quartzite slopes, occupied by small streams that appear unlikely to have cut such pronounced features (Photo 10). They may have been initiated along lines of weakness in the bedrock by subglacial meltwater streams and by meltwater during deglaciation.

Photo 8: Erratics of Canisp porphyry on a quartzite surface on the slopes of Canisp. Photo: Tim Lawson.

Photo 9: Crossing striations on a quartzite rock surface below Meallan Liath Beag. *Traces of striations cut by the basal debris of the last ice sheet are cut by a stronger striation trend cut under the ice of the Stronchrubie glacier in the Loch Lomond Stadial. Photo: Tim Lawson.*

Photo 10: Gorge carrying the drainage of the Allt Mhic Mhurchaidh Ghèir. *Photo: Tim Lawson.*

Periglacial features

The glacially abraded surfaces become progressively more frost-shattered as one ascends the slope until, at around 500m, the ground becomes dominated by **blockfields** and other frost-derived features (Photo 11). Surface water lying in joints in the rock expands when it freezes, wedging apart the rock which eventually breaks after numerous freeze-thaw cycles. The depth of this bouldery debris has been shown to be over 2m on certain slopes. Boulder lobes are well represented on the western side of Meallan Liath Mór (NC 223187) and on the northern flanks of Meall Diamhain on Canisp (NC 215182). They represent tongues of blocky debris that have been rafted down the hillside by the growth of ice between the particles and by the melting of the surface layer of the ground during short summer months. Together with the extensive blockfields, these are indicative of permafrost conditions that existed during the downwastage of the Late Devensian ice sheet and were reinitiated during the Loch Lomond Stadial. A small area of large-scale (1-2m diameter) patterned ground in the form of sorted stone nets, with mossy vegetation growing on the smaller stones in their centres, occurs at NC 212181 and supports this evidence. The growth of stratified ice lenses in the surface layers is believed progressively to displace larger particles towards the edge of the deforming ground as it heaves and relaxes, leaving smaller particles in the centre. Other smaller-scale periglacial features occur above 600m. Where a finer-grained mantle of weathered debris has developed, such as where igneous intrusions crop out, frost creep and solifluction have caused material to move slowly downhill, rolling up the vegetation mat to create turf-banked terraces with gravel treads aligned obliquely across the slope. The selective stripping of vegetation from debris-covered surfaces has created deflation stripes at NC 213182. Several ploughing boulders,

Photo 11: *Quartzite blockfields on Canisp.* *Looking across Meall Diamhain towards the distant mountains of Conival and Ben More Assynt. Photo: Tim Lawson.*

Photo 12: Looking downslope along the furrow created by a ploughing block on Canisp.
Photo: Tim Lawson.

whose movement downslope has cut a long furrow in their imperceptibly slow wake (Photo 12), have been found around NC 205184 and NC 213181. These are usually seen as good evidence for active solifluction, as are the small vegetated solifluction lobes occurring at 830m near the summit of Canisp (Photo 13). In numerous locations above 600m, where gravel-sized and smaller particles are available, active frost-sorting is manifest in the form of small sorted stone circles and nets up to about 60cm in diameter; the repeated frost-churning and uncovering of new stones in the centre of the nets contrasts with the lichen-covered and weathered patina of stones around their edges.

Moraines

On the lower slopes of the west side of the Loanan Valley, opposite Stronchrubie, a chaotic area of moraines and other till hummocks is being progressively eroded by the main river. A pronounced heather-covered ridge runs from near the road at NC 247189 to the

Photo 13: Active solifluction lobes near the summit of Canisp. Photo: Tim Lawson.

footbridge at NC 244191. Although partly a sloping outcrop of quartzite in its lowest levels, it appears to be otherwise composed of bouldery glacial till that may be part of a terminal moraine. Much more convincing is the arcuate feature at NC 242202 comprising three distinct ridges, 4m high on the steep eastern side and more gently sloping on the west (Photo 14). A distinct lateral moraine can be traced from its southern end up to a pronounced rock crag. It was formed by a lobe of ice flowing down from beneath Meallan Liath Beag that bulldozed up glacial debris in the valley bottom. This lobe of ice was part of a larger glacier that developed on the slopes between Meallan Liath Beag and Meallan Liath Mór during the Loch Lomond Stadial, whose extent can be determined from the distribution of glacial striations (Figure 5) indicating a well-defined ice flow descending the local slopes, cutting across the regional trend of striations noted above.

Access

The River Loanan can be crossed by footbridges near Loch Awe or opposite Stronchrubie (NC 244191). Once you have left the clinging blanket bog, walking is very straightforward over the glaciated rock surfaces, although care must be taken when walking over the blockfields as the boulders can be loose. The summit of Canisp is often covered in cloud, and its ascent in such conditions is not recommended in view of the extreme steepness of the sides of this mountain. A weather forecast should be obtained before setting out. The land in this area is part of the Assynt Estate, and deer-stalking takes place here from mid-July until mid-October. You are advised to let the Estate Office in Lochinver know if you are planning to visit the above area (Tel: 01571 844203). Allow at least five hours for a trip taking in all the features mentioned in this section.

Photo 14: The ridges of the terminal moraine in the Loanan Valley. The moraine complex curves away to the left around a grassy hollow. Photo: Tim Lawson.

LOCHAN TUATH

On the north face of Ben Mór Coigach (NC 1004) and either side of Sgùrr an Fhidhleir (NC 0905), a number of steep-sided corries and rockwalls have acted as the source areas for three small glaciers during the Loch Lomond Stadial (Figure 6). These glaciers extended out into a glacial diffluence trough cut in successive glaciations by ice streams that flowed between Ben Mór Coigach and Beinn an Eòin. Protruding above the thicker blanket bog in the valley bottom, bedrock surfaces of Torridonian sandstone have been sculpted by the ice. There are several good examples of classic *roches moutonnées* in the vicinity of NC 138054. Rock debris frozen into the basal layers of ice flowing towards the west has abraded the sandstone surfaces, smoothing and grooving them in the direction of ice flow. Finer striations that originally existed have since been weathered away, but the deeper examples remain. Strain that built up in the rock has led to

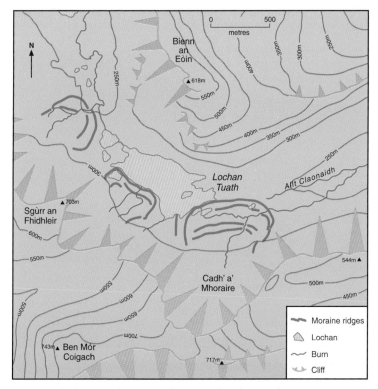

Figure 6: The location of moraine ridges around Lochan Tuath.

27

fracturing on the down-ice side of bedrock protuberances where pressure was lower, especially where cavities in the ice developed in the lee of the rock lump. Loosened rock fragments were frozen on to the basal ice and removed.

On the floor of the glaciated trough in front of the impressive rockwalls and buttresses of sandstone that comprise the truncated valley side lies a series of terminal moraines, nested one within the other (Photo 15). The outermost moraines are 4-6m high, slightly steeper on their eastern and northern sides. The inner moraine ridges are in places equally pronounced, but infilling of the troughs between them with peat and glacial debris has often reduced their original height. All the moraines are littered with Torridonian sandstone boulders. The presence of Lochan Tuath (NC 1005), occupying a rock basin near the watershed of the glaciated diffluence trough, has served to accentuate the moraines deposited by former glaciers emanating from the large corrie of Cadh' a' Mhoraire (NC 1004) and the eastern face of Sgùrr an Fhidhleir, as the lake has partially drowned the inter-moraine troughs.

The moraines are best viewed from either the top of the steep slope leading to the lip of the corrie (NC 108050) or from part way up the southern flank of Beinn an Eòin, depending on the light conditions. The Cadh' a' Mhoraire glacier deposited four distinct moraine ridges. Together with similar evidence from the adjoining areas and elsewhere in the region, these moraines clearly demonstrate that the

Photo 15: Ben Mór Coigach and the corrie of Cadh' a' Mhoraire. *The nested moraines described in the text can be clearly seen in the middle of the image. Photo: Tim Lawson.*

Loch Lomond Readvance glaciers remained glaciologically active for some time after reaching their greatest extent, each recessional moraine marking successive stable ice-marginal positions during the retreat of the ice. Moraines do not mark the later phases of retreat, so the ice may then have rapidly decayed *in situ*.

Access

This land is owned and managed by the Scottish Wildlife Trust and crofters. There are generally few problems of access in this area, although advice can be sought from the Trust by telephoning 01463 714746 during office hours. Vehicles can be parked in one of two large passing places at NC 146060. Be careful not to obstruct the passing place completely. The land is very poorly drained, so waterproof walking boots are necessary. Allow a minimum of four hours for the return trip.

BEINN AN FHURAIN

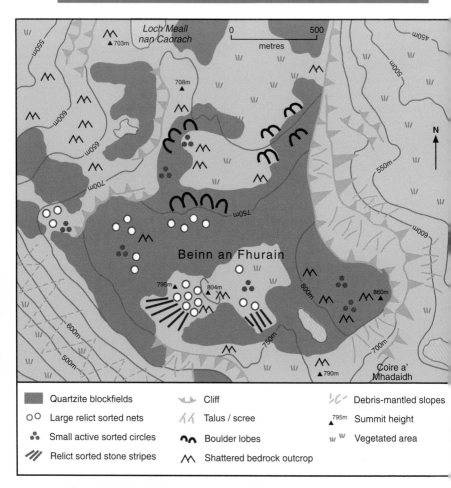

Figure 7: Periglacial features on Beinn an Fhurain.

This mountain exhibits some of the best preserved periglacial landforms in northern Scotland (Figure 7). The presence of Lewisian gneiss erratics indicates that it was eventually covered by the Late Devensian ice sheet, flowing broadly south-east to north-west, with its uppermost 40m protruding from the ice. Intense frost weathering and sorting in a harsh, periglacial environment as the ice sheet downwasted created a suite of landforms indicative of permafrost which, although reactivated during the Loch Lomond Stadial, remain as relict features today.

Underlain by frost-susceptible quartzite, frost-shattering of rock surfaces during the Late Devensian has covered the undulating plateau in an extensive blockfield. The open structure of boulders on the surface has been shown to give way to coarse boulders with an infill of silt-rich fine sediment at depth. This decrease of particle size with depth, together with the presence of both relict and active patterned ground features, is evidence of vertical frost-sorting under periglacial conditions. The patterned ground consists of a network of boulders encircling cells of mainly finer sediment (many vegetated with moss), some 2-4m in diameter with sorting extending down to depths of 0.6m. As slope gradient increases, these nets become more elongated and eventually give way to poorly-developed stone stripes on slopes greater than 7.5° (Figure 16). Active frost sorting is also evident in areas where stones are small and fine sediment is abundant, such as where igneous intrusions crop out at the surface. Small sorted nets and circles, with diameters of 15-60cm and sorting not exceeding 20cm depth, are accentuated as the smaller stones in the centre of the nets have clean, lichen-free surfaces in comparison to the weathered surfaces of the larger stones which surround them. The processes of formation of both large and small-scale patterned ground have been

Photo 16: Relict sorted stone nets tending towards stone stripes on Beinn an Fhurain. Photo: Tim Lawson.

Photo 17: Hummocky moraines on the lower ground east of Beinn an Fhurain.
Photo: Tim Lawson.

the subject of much debate. Many researchers suggest that they have been created by some form of heaving mechanism in the finer sediments in the centre of the nets. This may be associated with the growth of ice lenses as the patterned ground often occurs in slight depressions where drainage is poor. As surface heave occurs, followed by relaxation when the ice melts, larger particles are progressively displaced towards the outside of the nets over a large number of heave/relaxation events. The large, relict features are indicative of permafrost conditions, forming in the active surface layer where temperatures rose above freezing during the short summer months.

Protruding above the blockfields are frost-shattered tors of quartzite bedrock whose broad shape often indicates moulding by glacial erosion, further evidence that the last ice sheet overtopped most of this area. The flanks of the hill are mantled with blocky debris and active talus slopes. Solifluction and other **creep** processes have caused tongues of boulders to move downslope to form relict lobes several metres long and up to 1.3m high around the edge. Many good examples occur between 600-700m.

The eastern side of the plateau is marked by an abrupt free face flanked by talus, which formed the source area for a large glacier during the Loch Lomond Stadial. This former glacier flowed for some 3.5km eastwards, depositing the extensive areas of hummocky moraines (Photo 17), littered with boulders, that cover the boggy ground between Beinn an Fhurain and Gorm Loch Mór (NC 3124) and Fionn Loch Mór (NC 3323) where a number of terminal moraine ridges were deposited.

Access

This ground is rough so stout boots are essential. As the weather can deteriorate rapidly, especially on higher ground, ensure you have appropriate waterproof clothing. Vehicles can be parked in the car park near the Inchnadamph Hotel (NC 253217), and the plateau reached by following first the gravel track then the stalkers' path marked on the OS map along the valley of the Allt Poll an Droighinn for approximately 8km, branching left (at NC 274240) up to Loch nan Cuaran then continuing south over increasingly easier terrain. Alternatively, climb due east obliquely up the hillside behind Glenbain Cottage (NC 264217). Access may be restricted in this area during the deer-stalking season, primarily from mid-July to mid-October. Heed warning notices and take advice from the Assynt Estate Office in Lochinver (Tel: 01571 844203). Allow six hours for a round trip.

TRALIGILL VALLEY

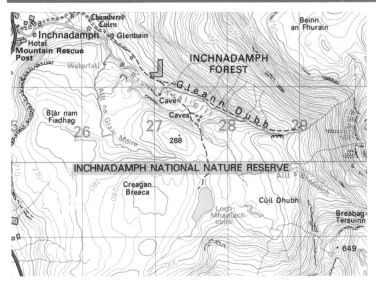

© Crown Copyright

The 5km-long Traligill River and its tributaries drain the basin formed by the high ground of Beinn an Fhurain (NC 2921), Conival (3019) and Breabag (2918). Much of this area is floored in dolomitic limestone, resulting in a **karst** landscape in a unique highland setting. This area is part of the Moine Thrust Belt, and repeated thrusting of slices of land have piled up one upon the other to create the Assynt mountains. The piling up of slices of the relatively thin layers of limestone has formed sufficient thickness of this rock to allow the development of subterranean water drainage and cave systems. Surface drainage from the surrounding quartzite bedrock starts to seep away into gravel-covered stream beds as soon as these streams reach the limestone outcrop. The high rainfall in this mountainous area means that many streams tend to flow for some distance onto the limestone in normal flow conditions, although dry stream beds are common after a prolonged period of reduced rain.

Water sinks and dry channels

One of the most impressive swallow-holes in the area is Cùil Dhubh Sink (NC 282194) (Photo 18). An unnamed river drains the slopes of Breabag and flows through the natural amphitheatre of Cùil Dhubh before entering a **blind valley** with steep sides, 10m high.

Photo 18: The blind valley of Cùil Dhubh Sink. Photo: Tim Lawson.

The water sinks into a 1m-square hole in the limestone in the south-west corner of the depression, and can back-up to form a large, peaty-brown lake in conditions of high runoff. In the north bank of the stream just before the sink, a channel leads to two large enclosed depressions, again around 10m deep in places, separated by an igneous intrusion. When the flow of water exceeds the capacity of Cùil Dhubh Sink, floodwater spills over into these depressions then eventually drains away through the bouldery glacial till occupying their floors. At any one time a number of holes and collapses in the till can be seen, indicating the route taken by the last flood as scouring water drained away.

The Allt a' Bhealaich drains the steep slopes of Conival and the Bhealach Traligil. A number of small water sinks occur in its bed before it peters out at approximately NC 282198. Thereafter its channel is often dry in the summer months as far as NC 281200, where a small intermittent stream proceeds towards Cnoc nan Uamh (NC 278204). Floodwater sinks away in large peat-floored depressions. The stream is a mere trickle as it proceeds north-westwards before falling into an open pothole at Uamh Cailliche Peireag (NC 276203) where a waterfall has cut backwards to intersect part of a cave system (Photo 19). Another small stream is swallowed by Pipe Sink (NC 287200), although interconnecting relict channels, perennially dry and completely vegetated, extend from here to connect with the seasonally dry Allt a' Bhealaich channel, suggesting that it used to flow across the surface before an underground route was established. Downvalley from Uamh Cailliche Peireag the channel of the Allt a' Bhealaich is normally dry, cut across the dip of a major thrust plane. Further small relict channels, again completely vegetated, join the dry channel's north bank, testimony of more extensive surface runoff in the past.

The Traligill River itself follows the line of Gleann Dubh beneath Beinn an Fhurain, fed by the high rainfall and rapid water runoff from the quartzite, before turning sharply south-west and sinking at Lower Traligill Cave (NC 271209). For the next 0.5km the Traligill's channel is seasonally dry, wedged between the exposed thrust-plane surface and a pronounced cliff (Photo 20). Drainage water runs parallel to the surface channel but farther down the thrust plane, deeper into the cliff at a number of discrete levels. As runoff discharges increase, water moves progressively higher up the thrust plane until it once more flows in the river channel. Figure 8 shows how a rise in water table creates a temporary river under conditions of high discharge.

Photo 19: Uamh Cailliche Peireag. *Here a retreating waterfall has intersected with a truncated cave passage. Water now enters the cave via a swallow-hole, and resurges here in times of high discharge. Photo: Tim Lawson.*

Photo 20: Traligill Valley: *looking south-east along the inclined thrust plane exposed in the central part of the valley, between Lower Traligill Cave and Traligill Rising (where the water is resurging). Photo: Tim Lawson.*

Cave systems

The dominant cave system in the drainage basin is that which runs through Cnoc nan Uamh ('Hill of the Caves'). There are three main entrances to the system (NC 276206). Uamh an Tartair ('Cave of the Roaring') has a small entrance chamber that leads down to the

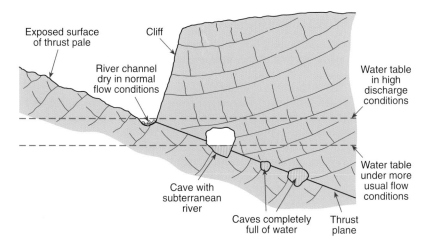

Figure 8: Hypothetical cross-section of the Traligill River's channel, *between Lower Traligill Cave and Traligill Rising.*

active streamway and on into a large, complex series of passageways: the urge for the casual visitor to explore must be resisted, as the lack of knowledge of a cave's layout together with a lack of specific caving equipment will compromise safety. The cave extends back through the hill, and it is thought that the choked passages in Uamh Cailliche Peireag are part of the same cave system. The other two main entrances are Uamh an Uisge ('Cave of the Water' – known locally as 'The Waterslide') and an open pothole. Water from Uamh an Tartair cascades impressively down an inclined thrust plane for some 80m before meeting a sump pool where the cave is flooded to its roof.

Lower Traligill Cave (NC 271209) has developed on two levels of a major thrust plane, whose outcrop can be clearly seen to the left of the cave entrance. The lower level is an active streamway, being frequently sumped and accessible in only extremely dry conditions: water levels can rise alarmingly quickly here if it has rained recently on Conival or Beinn an Fhurain, trapping the unwary visitor! The upper level is usually dry, and contains a variety of speleothem deposits including flowstone, stalagmites and fragile, convoluted stalactites called helictites.

Limestone pavements

These are not well developed in Assynt due partly to frost action and also to the steeply-inclined dip of the thin beds of limestone. A small area of denuded pavement with characteristic blocks of limestone (clints) separated by solutionally-enlarged joints (grykes) can be seen in the valley of the Allt na Glaic Mòire around NC 266253. However, the best development of this type of landform occurs on the exposed thrust plane in the Traligill Valley, downstream of Lower Traligill Cave. Here surface waters have dissolved the limestone surface into many fretted and abstract shapes (Photo 21).

Water resurgences and gorges

In flood conditions, when the capacity of subterranean routeways in the middle section of the drainage basin is exceeded, water flow is reversed at Lower Traligill Cave and resurges at its entrance to flow down the seasonally-dry channel. In normal summer conditions, the main water resurgence for most of the water from the upper and middle basin is Traligill Rising (NC 267212) (Photo 20). Downstream of this point, the Traligill is a permanent river. A further resurgence occurs in the river bed just downstream of the footbridge at NC 265212. Between these two resurgences, the river occupies a striking gorge, possibly formed by headward erosion of the seasonally-dry waterfall above Traligill Rising.

The lower reaches of the Traligill flow in a narrow gorge where the river has cut through the successive thrust masses of limestone rather than sub-parallel to the thrust planes as it tends to do farther up the valley. A number of water resurgences have been identified in the river by dye-tracing techniques, notably Waterfall Rising at NC 264215

Photo 21: Solutional features weathered into the limestone surface of the exposed thrust plane. Photo: Tim Lawson.

and Firehose Cave at NC 264216; the spectacular discharge from the latter is partly derived from subterranean drainage down a thrust plane from the quartzite slopes on the north side of the valley by way of Glenbain Hole (NC 265217).

Access

As this land is part of the Inchnadamph National Nature Reserve there are few access restrictions throughout the year, although care should be taken in the deer-stalking season (mid-July to mid-October). Vehicles can be parked in the car park west of the Inchnadamph Hotel (NC 251216), and the gravel track up to Glenbain Cottage (NC 264217) is easy walking. Thereafter, bear right by the old sheepfold to follow a footpath that goes right up to Uamh an Tartair. A narrow footpath leads around the south side of Cnoc nan Uamh and past Uamh Cailliche Peireag, before degenerating into a peaty path that leads to Loch Mhaolach-coire (NC 2719). A low, heather-covered dyke leads from the east side of the loch directly to Cùil Dhubh Sink. Thereafter a return journey follows the floodwater depressions, the Allt a' Bhealaich until it joins the Traligill River, and then via Lower Traligill Cave, Traligill Rising and back across the field to Glenbain Cottage to regain the gravel track. The importance of not venturing into the caves without a guide and proper caving equipment cannot be overstressed: cave rescue is co-ordinated from Edinburgh, and it would be many hours before a rescue team could be assembled in this remote area. Do not put yourself at risk.

THE ALLT NAN UAMH VALLEY

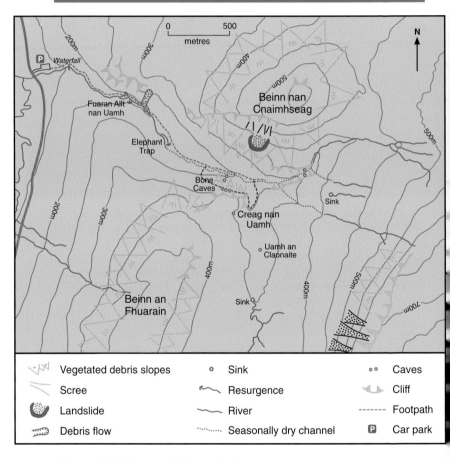

Figure 9: Main features of Allt nan Uamh.

The Allt nan Uamh ('Burn of the Caves') (NC 2617) drains the quartzite slopes of Fuarain Ghlasa and Creag Liath and the southern end of Breabag. Aligned as it is along the direction of flow of the last ice sheet, both repeated glaciation and fluvial erosion have incised a deep valley, cutting through part of the Ben More thrust sheet into the limestone beneath. This has left Beinn nan Cnaimhseag to the north and Beinn an Fhuarain to the south as Torridonian sandstone and Cambrian quartzite remnants of the original mass of thrust rock. As drainage water flows from the impermeable quartzite to the east onto the permeable limestone, it starts to seep away into fissures in the latter beneath the boulders flooring the river bed. The river channel is therefore usually dry for part of its length, between approximately NC 276173 and NC 262176, depending on runoff conditions (Figure 9). A number of water resurgences occur along its length, the two most impressive being Fuaran Allt nan Uamh (NC 261177) where water emerges in a torrent from cracks at the base of a small cliff, and The Elephant Trap (NC 264174), a 1.5m-deep depression in the boulders next to the main channel from which water wells up under pressure (Photo 22). The presence of these resurgences, and others in the vicinity, is due to the intersection of a major fault plane (visible as a small notch on the southern edge of the Creag nan Uamh) and a sheet of intruded, dark-green igneous rock near the base of the limestone. The fault plane acts as the main aquifer for water draining the southern half of the drainage basin, and the impermeable igneous rock forces the water back on to the surface. The river tumbles over a 4m-high waterfall at NC 256179 at the edge of the igneous intrusion (see frontispiece).

Hillslope features

The lower parts of the valley sides are composed of a layer of bouldery glacial till overlying limestone. This till mantle is thickest on the valley floor where it is being eroded by the river and its tributaries. A number of fresh sections through the deposits are exposed where fluvial erosion has caused small collapses. Elsewhere, similar older features have become stabilised and vegetated by grasses

Photo 22: Water resurging from The Elephant Trap in the Allt nan Uamh Valley.
The seasonally dry river bed is visible in the background. Photo: Tim Lawson.

and heather. The thinner drift cover on the steeper slopes is prone to failure, as evidenced by the debris slide just up-valley from Fuaran Allt nan Uamh (NC 261176): small gullies funnel water into the top of the feature, saturating the till which has slid downslope, creating a fan of coarse gravel and cobbles next to the river channel.

The slopes beneath Beinn nan Cnaimhseag are composed of rockfall talus forming a sheet of angular debris of sandstone and quartzite. This is believed to have formed during downwastage of the Late

Photo 23: The complex landslide beneath the summit of Beinn nan Cnaimhseag.
Photo: Tim Lawson.

Devensian ice sheet and also during the Loch Lomond Stadial due to frost-shattering of bedrock surfaces in the harsh periglacial climate. They are now almost completely vegetated with heather: where the talus is exposed it is clearly stabilised, as shown by the lichen-covered faces of the rocky debris. This contrasts markedly with the upper part of the slope beneath the summit of the hill, where an apron of coarse, bouldery debris forming broad lobes occurs (Photo 23). This has been interpreted as a landslide reflecting weaknesses along the upper part of the slope where the rocks have been crushed and fractured by tectonic movement along the Ben More Thrust Plane. It is likely that initiation of the landslide was at least partly due to the effect of the removal of confining pressures once the area became deglaciated. A thin layer of the affected material slid and partly flowed down the slope, coming to rest against prominent bosses of limestone that project out of the hillside here. Subsequent frost action in the Holocene has shattered material from the newly-formed cliff at the top of the slope, forming fresh talus cones on top of the landslide debris. Slab failure from the cliff has littered the landslide with large blocks.

Creag nan Uamh

This imposing crag of limestone (Photo 24) dominates the middle part of the valley. A largely vegetated talus slope rises steeply from the south side of the river channel up to the foot of the crag at around 330m. Here three large cave entrances (Badger Cave, Reindeer Cave and Bone Cave from west to east) lead roughly

Photo 24: Creag nan Uamh from the upper slopes of Beinn nan Cnaimhseag. *The Bone Caves are visible in the shadow at the top of the vegetated talus slope in the right-central part of the crag. Lower down the slope, above the seasonally-dry river channel, are the entrances to Otter Hole and Lower Otter Hole. Photo: Tim Lawson.*

Photo 25: Caves on Creag nan Uamh *from the north side of the Allt nan Uamh Valley. Here the Bone Caves can be seen at the top of the vegetated talus slope and Otter Hole and Lower Otter Hole below, indicating later resurgence levels as water tables fell following repeated glacial downcutting of the main valley floor. Photo: Tim Lawson.*

horizontally into the hillside. Known collectively as the 'Bone Caves', they are part of a large cave system that formed beneath the water table before glacial erosion of the valley below breached the sandstone and quartzite capping the limestone, allowing the groundwater to drain to a lower level. Successive phases of deepening of the valley are marked by a further two levels of smaller horizontal cave passages (Otter Hole and Lower Otter Hole) below the Bone Caves, best viewed from the path in the valley bottom (Photo 25).

These caves, truncated by the formation of the valley, are all choked with sediment at various distances into the hill. Cavers and cave divers have explored Uamh an Claonaite (Scotland's longest cave system, whose entrance at NC 271166 and upper passageways lie at about the same altitude as the Bone Caves), discovering a vast network of chambers and passages within Creag nan Uamh. Uranium-series dating of speleothems from Uamh an Claonaite suggest that the oldest parts of the cave are more than 200,000 years old, implying a similar age for the Bone Caves.

The Bone Caves were excavated in 1926-27 after an initial excavation of one of them in 1889. They have yielded human remains recently dated to the Neolithic period, but they are more important for the huge amount of animal remains that were recovered, including the remains of lynx, brown bear, reindeer, wolf, and various small rodents, some of which are indicative of harsh arctic conditions. The skull of a bear, now thought possibly to be a polar bear and radiocarbon dated to around 18,900 years ago, found in the inner chamber of Reindeer Cave, is now on display in the Museum of Scotland in Edinburgh, and is only the second skeletal fragment of this animal yet discovered in Britain.

Access

The Allt nan Uamh Valley forms the southern edge of the Inchnadamph National Nature Reserve, and there are no access restrictions at any time. There is a car park on the eastern side of the A837 at NC 254179 from where an upgraded footpath leads past all the features mentioned above. Where the footpath splits, take the right hand fork and cross the dry river bed to climb steadily up to the Bone Caves. The path, narrow and a little exposed in places, continues around the foot of the crag and descends a dry valley to rejoin the other path on the north side of the river channel. Allow two hours for this circular walk.

Please note that the Creag nan Uamh is a Scheduled Ancient Monument, so unauthorised digging is illegal.

THE STOER PENINSULA

The thick beds of Torridonian sandstone that form this peninsula have been attacked by stormy seas to produce a wonderful cliffed coastline, particularly in the north. Erratic boulders of Lewisian gneiss indicate that the area was completely covered by the Late Devensian ice sheet, flowing towards the west-north-west. A mantle of sandy glacial till covers the sandstone outcrop, producing a smoothed, grass-covered landscape in striking contrast to the knurled gneiss outcrop to the east and south. In a few sheltered localities, such as Clashnessie Bay (NC 056310) and Bay of Culkein (NC 039332), fine sandy beaches have formed. On the eastern edge of the former, providing the site for the croft of Imirfada, a raised **tombolo** connects a former island to the mainland. This is fragmentary evidence for the highest level reached by the sea in the present interglacial period, which occurred when the land surface was still depressed from the weight of the former ice sheet although oceanic water volumes had increased as the ice sheets had melted. Beaches were formed along the coastline of the time, but land surfaces have continued to rise since then as they return to pre-glacial positions. As a result, raised shoreline features have been created. Elsewhere along this coast, dramatic erosion carried out on cliffed coastlines has removed any similar evidence.

The coastline north of the Bay of Culkein exhibits many features of the sequence of coastal erosion and cliff retreat. Primarily, erosion is greatest where areas of weakness exist in the rocks. In this location such weaknesses are near-vertical, small faultlines and major joints extend through the rock layers. Hydraulic action, whereby waves trap air in such fissures in the rock, causes the rock to be weakened as these fissures are forced deeper. At the same time solutional and abrasional processes attack the rock in the intertidal zone, undercutting the cliff and further widening lines of weakness. Eventually caves are created and enlarged, the lower parts of their walls being smoothed and undercut by coastal erosion processes whereas the upper parts of their walls and roofs are more angular, caused by breakdown and rockfall processes. Good examples can be seen just south of Rubh' an Dunain at NC 042339, together with a geo, a narrow chasm caused by the total collapse of a cave roof into the sea. Where caves are excavated along lines of weakness that cut through headlands, natural arches are formed. The arch that cuts through the Rubh' an Dunain promontory, upon which ancient people built a small fort, is only connected to the mainland by a bridge of shattered rock less than 1m wide (Photo 26).

Photo 26: The natural arch and marine abrasion platform at Rubh' an Dunain.
Photo: Tim Lawson.

As such arches are progressively enlarged, they eventually collapse to form stacks. These pillars of rock stranded offshore are eventually eroded down to stumps then obliterated entirely by wave action. The most impressive stack along this section of coastline is the Old Man of Stoer (NC 016352). Fifty metres high and surrounded by a churning sea, it can be viewed from the top of the 60m-high vertical cliff (Photo 27).

Wave energy becomes concentrated on headlands, whose cliffs are progressively undercut leading to cliff collapse and retreat. As the cliff is cut back, a rock platform lying between high and low tide marks is cut by abrasion and marked by solutional processes. A good example of this surrounds the Rubh' an Dunain promontory, and elsewhere around the Stoer coast, exposed at low tide.

At the crofting townships of Stoer and Clachtoll in the south-west of the peninsula, dunes of blown sand cover the bedrock to produce a well-drained grassy sward known as 'machair', for centuries a vital grazing resource for local people.

Photo 27: The Old Man of Stoer, *an impressive sea stack. Photo: Tim Lawson.*

Access

Vehicles can be parked near the old jetty at Culkein (NC 038333), from where Rubh' an Dunain can be reached by an easy 10-minute walk along the coast. Access to the Old Man of Stoer is more problematic, but vehicles driven along the rough and muddy track north-westwards out of Culkein can be parked at the north end of Loch Cùl Fraioch (NC 023335), and a rather boggy walk around the east side of Sidhean Mór eventually brings one to the cliff top close to the stack (NC 017352). Extreme care should be exercised here as the position is very exposed.

GLOSSARY

Blind valley. A valley that leads into a closed depression.

Blockfield. An area completely mantled with frost-shattered boulders so that little bedrock protrudes through.

Calcareous. Containing large amounts of calcium carbonate.

Corrie. A large, armchair-shaped hollow in a mountain side, created by glacial action.

Creep. Any slow, imperceptible movement of weathered rock debris down a hillslope under the influence of gravity.

Debris flow. Fluid mixture of rock debris and water, which flows downhill under the influence of gravity.

Diffluence trough. A glaciated valley that cuts through a former watershed.

Dolomitic limestone. Rock composed of dolomite, a carbonate of calcium and magnesium.

Dyke. Steeply dipping or vertical sheet of igneous rock, injected across the beds of a sedimentary rock.

Erratics. Boulders of rock that have been carried from their source onto a different type of rock.

Glacial friction cracks. A suite of curved cracks and notches on glaciated bedrock surfaces created by contact with large boulders being carried within the basal glacier ice.

Glacial striations. Minute scratches on glaciated rock surfaces, abraded by rock debris frozen on to the underside of a glacier or ice sheet.

Gneiss. An ancient, heavily metamorphosed rock characterised by its structure of alternate bands of quartz and feldspars (light) and mica and amphiboles (dark).

Igneous intrusion. An injection of molten rock into pre-existing rocks, that subsequently cools and hardens into igneous rock (see 'dyke' and 'sill').

Karst. Name given to the distinctive landscape features that form on and in limestone bedrock.

Metamorphic. Of rocks transformed in some way by heat or pressure.

Moraine. Any ridge or mound of glacial till.

Nunataks. Areas that protrude above the surface of an ice sheet.

Periglacial. Harshly cold climate, but a non-glacial environment.

Permafrost. Ground where the temperature is permanently below freezing, although a thin surface layer may thaw in the short summer months.

Quartzite. A hard, brittle metamorphic form of sandstone, composed of almost pure quartz.

Solifluction. Slow flowage of weathered debris down a slope.

Sill. Sheet-like mass of igneous rock, originally injected along bedding planes between sedimentary rock strata.

Speleothems. Chemically-precipitated rock formations found in caves (e.g. stalagmites and stalactites)

Stadial. A cold climatic phase within an overall glacial stage, with intervening more temperate interludes (interstadials) that are not as warm as true interglacial periods.

Talus. Loose debris piled up beneath free faces from which it has been prised (also called 'scree').

Till. Largely unsorted debris of mixed particle sizes, deposited by or from glacier ice.

Tombolo. Spit of sand or gravel linking an offshore island to the mainland.

BIBLIOGRAPHY

Ballantyne, C.K. and Harris, C. (1994) *The Periglaciation of Great Britain.* Cambridge: Cambridge University Press.

Ballantyne, C.K., McCarroll, D., Nesje, A., Dahl, S.O. and Stones, J.O. (1998) 'The last ice sheet in North-West Scotland: reconstruction and implications', *Quaternary Science Reviews*, 17, pp. 1149-84.

Johnson, M.R.W. and Parsons, I. (1979). *Macgregor and Phemister's Geological Guide to the Assynt District of Sutherland.* Edinburgh: Edinburgh Geological Society.

Johnstone, G.S. and Mykura, W. (1989) *The Northern Highlands of Scotland.* British Regional Geology (fourth edition). London: HMSO.

Hebdon, N.J., Atkinson, T.C., Lawson, T.J. and Young, I.R. (1997) 'Rate of valley deepening during the Late Quaternary in Assynt, Scotland', *Earth Surface Processes and Landforms*, 22, pp. 307-15.

Lawson, T.J. (1981) 'The 1926-7 excavation of the Creag nan Uamh bone caves, near Inchnadamph, Sutherland', *Proceedings of the Society of Antiquaries of Scotland*, 111, pp. 7-20.

Lawson, T.J. (1984) 'Reindeer in the Scottish Quaternary', *Quaternary Newsletter*, 42, pp. 1-7.

Lawson, T.J. (1986) 'Loch Lomond Advance glaciers in Assynt, Sutherland, and their palaeoclimatic implications', *Scottish Journal of Geology*, 22, pp. 289-98.

Lawson, T.J. (ed) (1988) *Caves of Assynt.* Edinburgh: Grampian Speleological Group.

Lawson, T.J. (1990) 'Former ice movement in Assynt, Sutherland, as shown by the distribution of glacial erratics', *Scottish Journal of Geology*, 26, pp. 25-32.

Lawson, T.J. (1993) 'Creag nan Uamh' in Gordon, J.E. and Sutherland, D.G. (eds) *Quaternary of Scotland: The Geological Conservation Review series, no. 6.* London: Chapman & Hall, pp. 127-33.

Lawson, T.J. (1995a) 'Boulder trains as indicators of former ice flow in Assynt, NW Scotland', *Quaternary Newsletter*, 75, pp. 15-22.

Lawson, T.J. (1995b) 'An analysis of sediments in caves in the Assynt area, NW Scotland', *Cave and Karst Science*, 22, pp. 23-30.

Lawson, T.J. (ed) (1995c) *The Quaternary of Assynt and Coigach: Field Guide.* Cambridge: Quaternary Research Association.

Lawson, T.J. (1996) 'Glacial striations and former ice movement: the evidence from Assynt, Sutherland', *Scottish Journal of Geology*, 32, pp. 59-65.

Lawson, T.J. and Bonsall, J.C. (1986a) 'Early settlement in Scotland: the evidence from Reindeer Cave, Assynt', *Quaternary Newsletter*, 49, pp. 1-7.

Lawson, T.J. and Bonsall, J.C. (1986b) 'The Palaeolithic in Scotland: a reconsideration of evidence from Reindeer Cave, Assynt' in Colcutt, S.N. (ed) *The Palaeolithic of Britain and its Nearest Neighbours: Recent Trends.* Sheffield: Department of Archaeology and Prehistory, University of Sheffield, pp. 85-9.

McCarroll, D., Ballantyne, C.K., Nesje, A. and Dahl, S.-O. (1995) 'Nunataks of the last ice sheet in north-west Scotland', *Boreas*, 24, pp. 305-23.

Murray, N.A., Bonsall, C., Sutherland, D.G., Lawson, T.J. and Kitchener A.C. (1993) 'Further radiocarbon determinations on reindeer remains of Middle and Late Devensian age from the Creag nan Uamh caves, Assynt, NW Scotland', *Quaternary Newsletter*, 70, pp. 1-10.

Peach, B.N. and Horne, J. (1917) 'The bone-cave in the valley of Allt nan Uamh (Burn of the Caves), near Inchnadamff, Assynt, Sutherlandshire', *Proceedings of the Royal Society of Edinburgh*, 37, pp. 327-48.

Peach, B.N., Horne, J., Gunn, W., Clough, C.T. and Hinxman, L.W. (1907) *The Geological Structure of the North-West Highlands of Scotland.* Memoir of the Geological Survey of Great Britain.

Sellier, D. and Lawson, T.J. (1998) 'A complex slope failure on Beinn nan Cnaimhseag, Assynt, Sutherland', *Scottish Geographical Magazine*, 114, pp. 85-93.

Sissons, J.B. (1977) 'The Loch Lomond Readvance in the northern mainland of Scotland' in Gray, J.M. and Lowe, J.J. (eds) *Studies in the Scottish Lateglacial Environment.* Oxford: Pergamon, pp. 45-59.